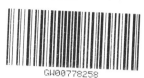

Eco Activities

METAL

Written by
Louise Nelson

BookLife PUBLISHING

©2022
BookLife Publishing Ltd.
King's Lynn
Norfolk, PE30 4LS, UK

A catalogue record for this book is available from the British Library.

ISBN: 978-1-83927-269-1

Written by:
Louise Nelson

Edited by:
Robin Twiddy

Designed by:
Jasmine Pointer

CONTENTS

Words that look like this can be found in the glossary on page 24.

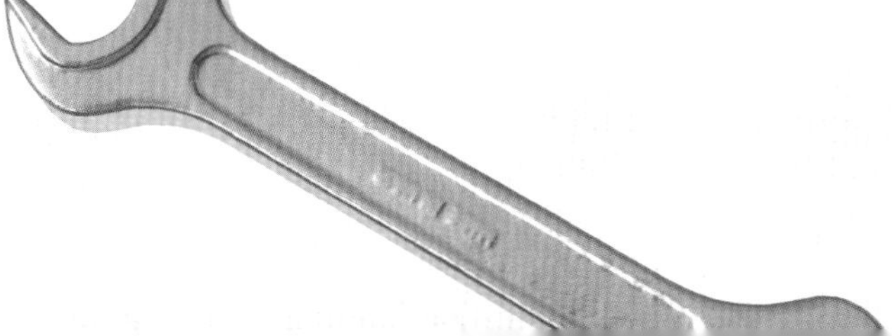

AMAZING METAL

Hold it right there! Don't chuck that can away! Tins and cans are so useful, but they are made of metal. This means they will stay in landfill for a long time!

Did you know?
A lot of things we think we should throw away can be used again and again!

Digging metal up from the ground is called mining. This process is very bad for the planet. It's important that we make the most of the metal we already have.

Reduce: Try not to buy more metal things.

Reuse: Use metal items again and again!

Make your own dog food to save cans!

Recycle: Make sure you recycle metal things.

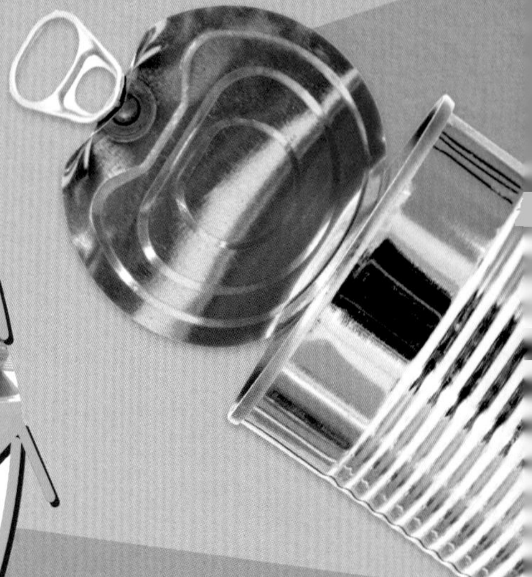

WHAT IS METAL?

Metal is a material. We use materials such as wood, glass, fabric and metal to make things. Materials have properties. Properties tell us what the material is like.

The Properties of Metal

Can be thin or thick

Made by people from a natural material

Hard and strong

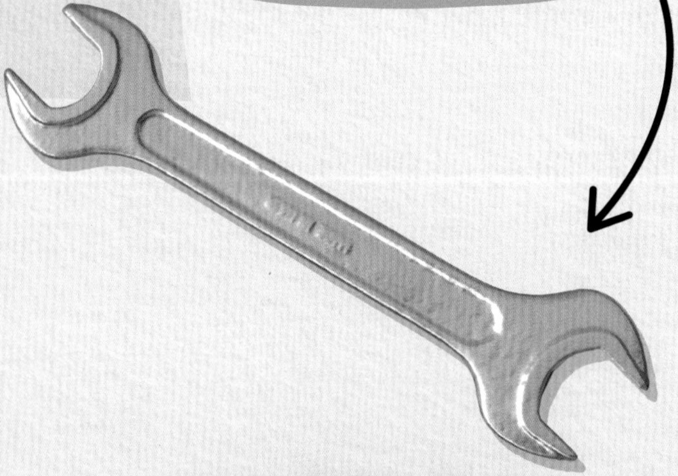

Opaque
(not see-through)

Waterproof

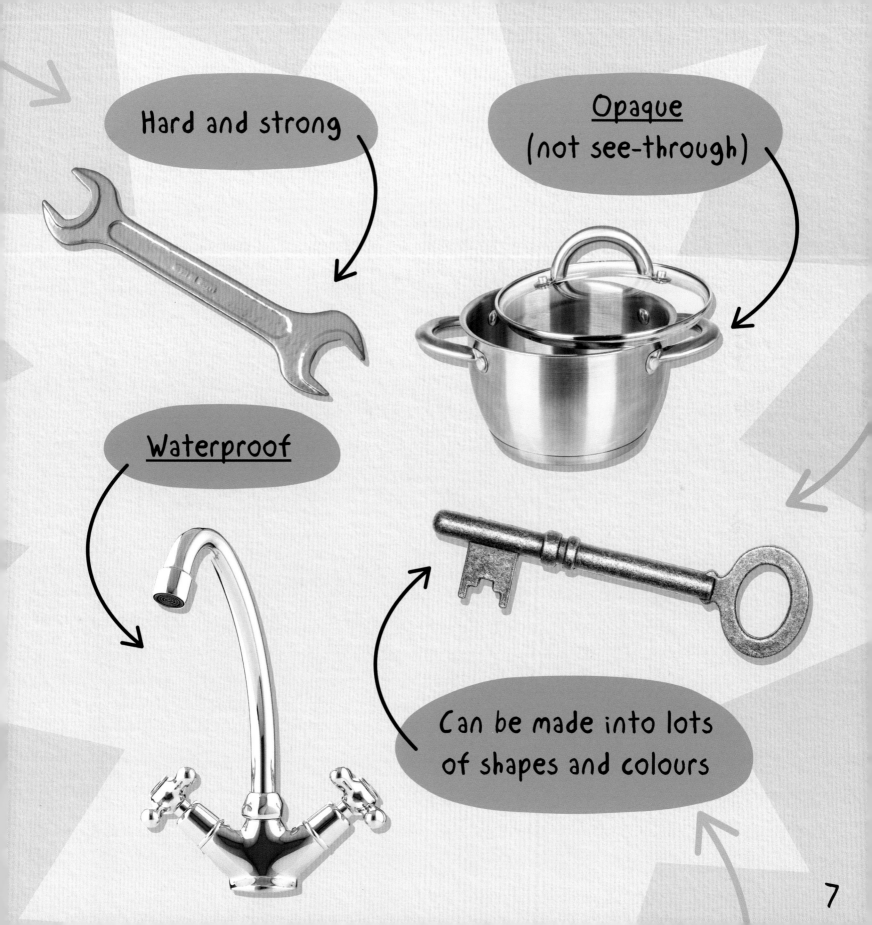

Can be made into lots of shapes and colours

CAN YOU HEAR ME?

Never mind mobile phones – have you ever talked on a tin can?

You can also make these with paper or plastic cups.

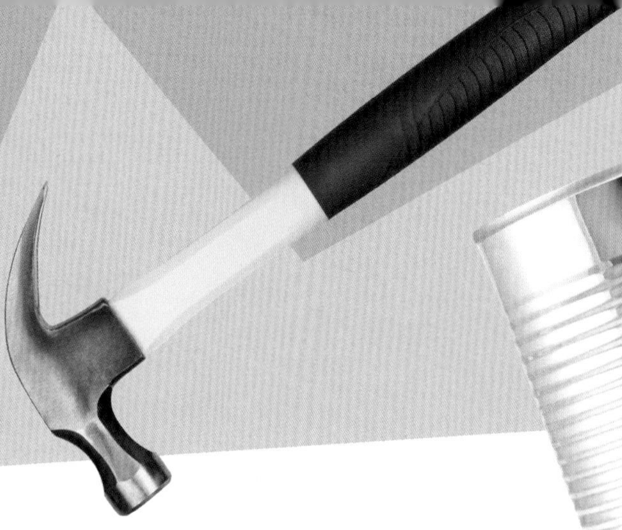

You will need:

- Two empty tin cans
- String (at least two metres)
- Paint (white and colours)
- Paintbrushes
- A hammer
- A nail
- Safety goggles
- A grown-up

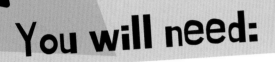

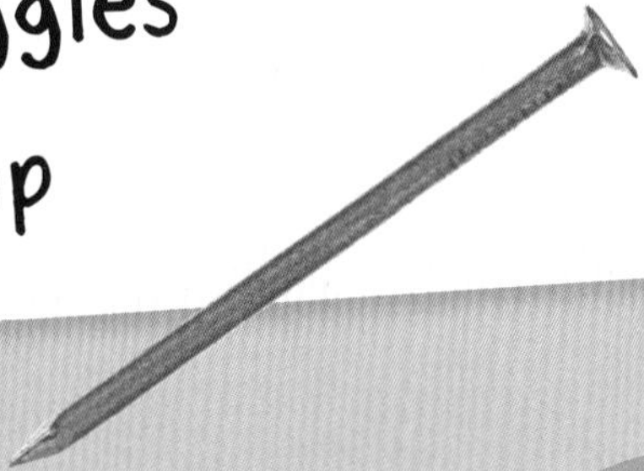

Safety First!

Make sure a grown-up opens the cans and makes sure there are no sharp edges. Wash your cans well and make sure they are dry.

STEP 1. Put on your goggles.

STEP 2. Get a grown-up to take off one end of the can and tap the nail into the other end of the can to make a hole, then carefully pull it out.

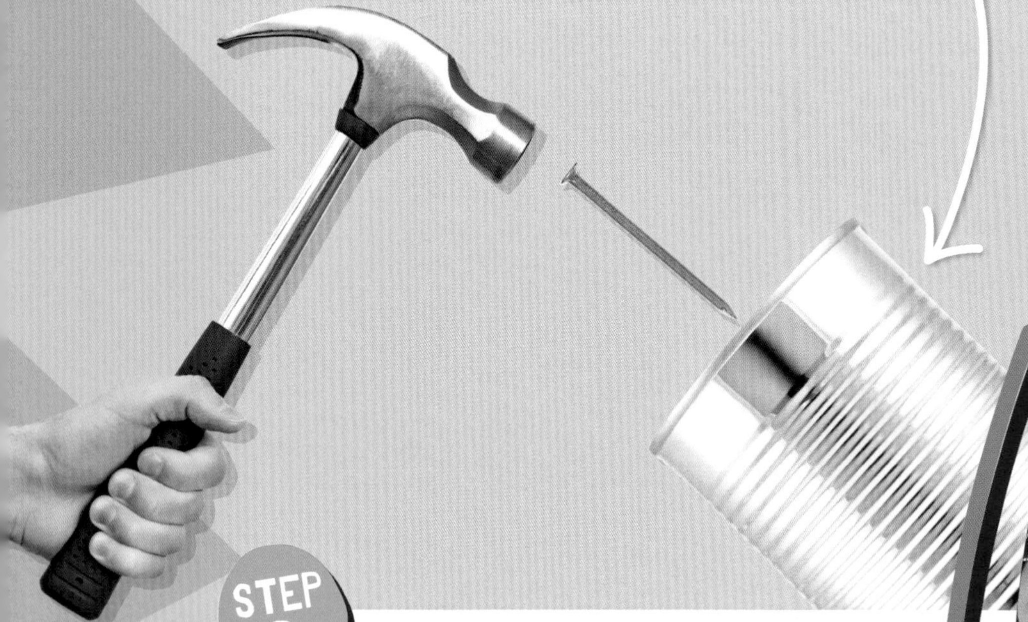

STEP 3. Paint your tin cans white and let them dry.

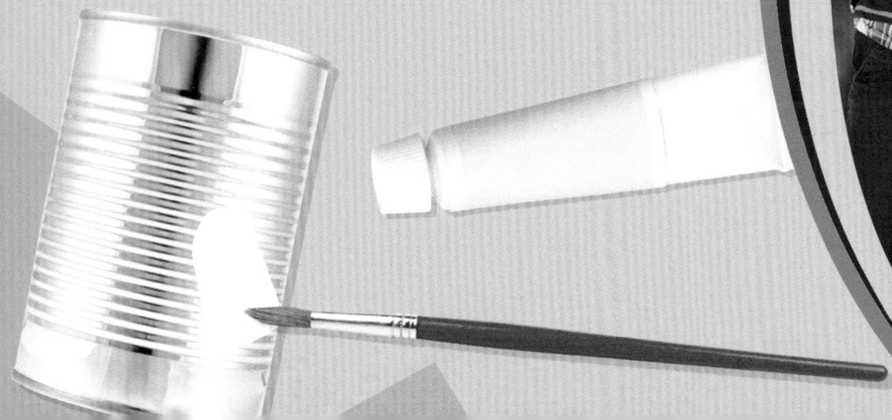

STEP 4. Paint them with any colours you want.

STEP 5. Thread the string between the two cans and tie a knot at each end so that the string can't fall out of the cans.

STEP 6. To use your telephone, stand as far apart as you can.

STEP 7. Keep the string tight, then take turns to talk into the cans, and listen for replies!

Your voice will travel along the string as a vibration. Wow!

I CAN FEED THE BIRDS

These colourful cans will brighten up a winter tree – and give the birds a winter treat!

Make sure your paint works on metal.

You will need:

- Empty cans
- Bird seeds and nuts
- Wooden sticks or fallen branches
- String
- Paint
- Paintbrushes
- A drill (for grown-ups only!)
- Hot glue gun

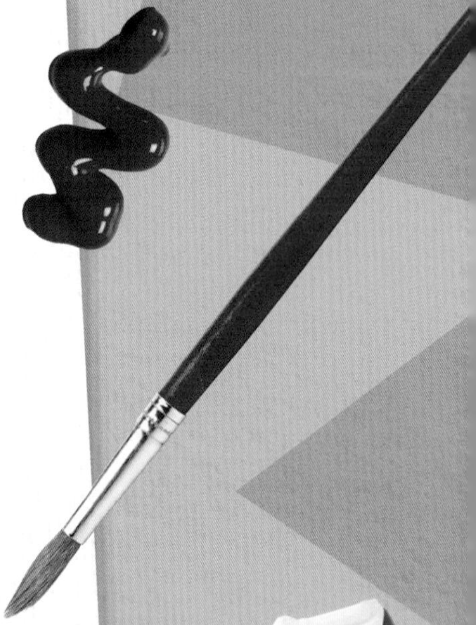

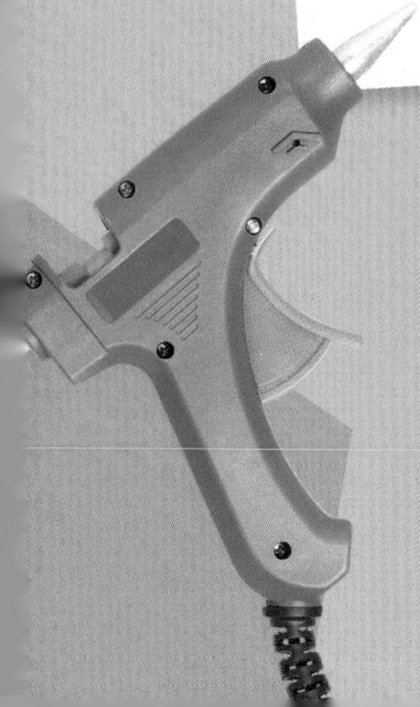

STEP 1. Clean and paint your cans.

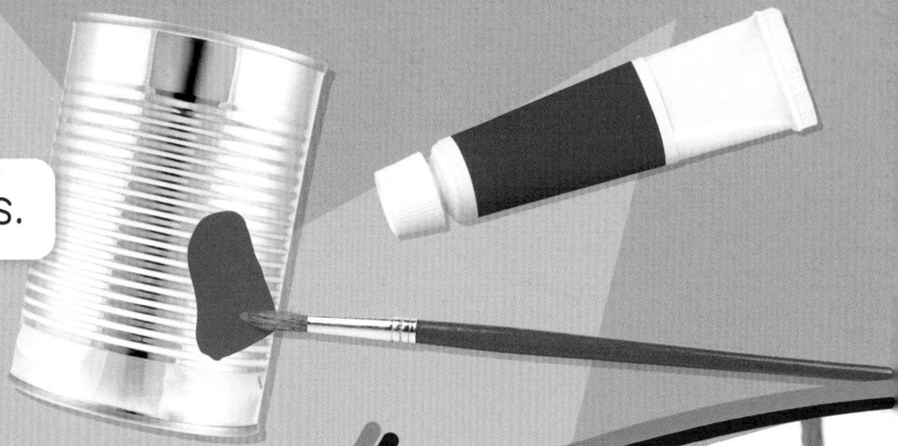

STEP 2. Ask a grown-up to make a hole in the bottom of the can, near to the edge. Your stick needs to fit into the hole, so they may need to carefully use a drill.

STEP 3. Poke your stick a small way through the hole.

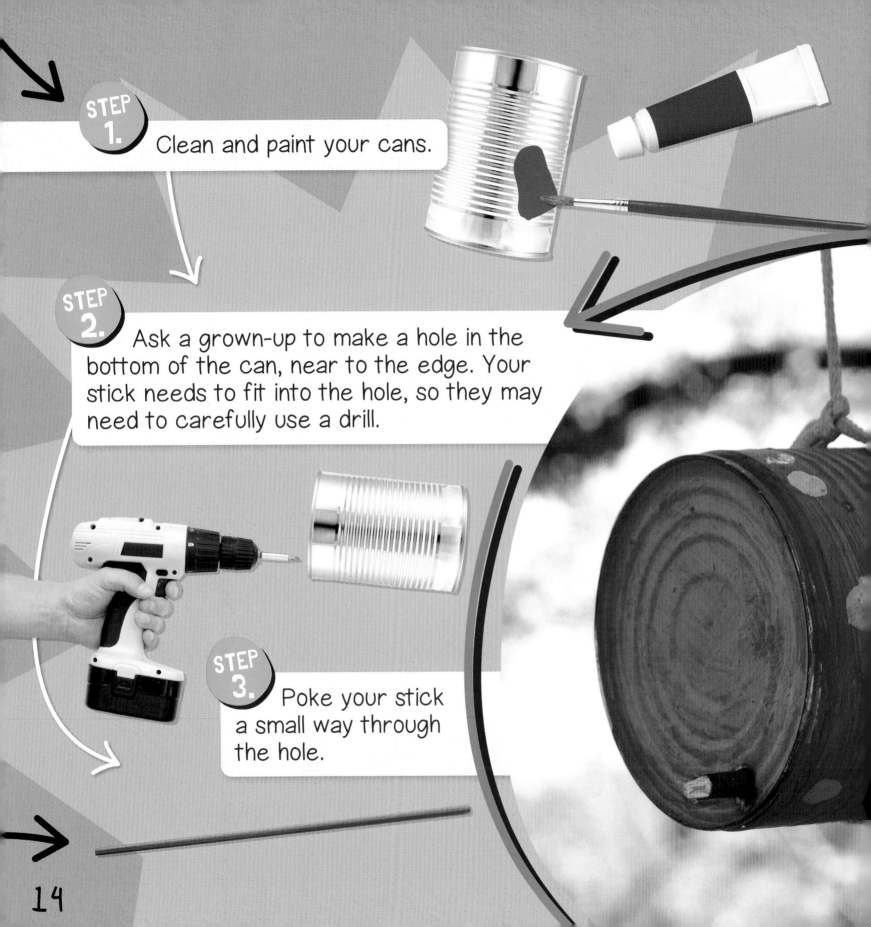

STEP 4. Ask a grown-up to glue the stick down along the length of the can inside.

STEP 5. Tie string around the middle of the can.

STEP 6. Put in a handful of bird seeds and nuts and hang in your tree!

Don't forget – you can't recycle metal that has been painted. Make sure you only paint what you need, then recycle the rest.

METAL MADNESS

If we throw metal things such as cans and scrap metal into landfill, they take a very long time to rot away. Luckily, metal can easily be recycled. This means it will be used to make something new.

Even cars can be recycled!

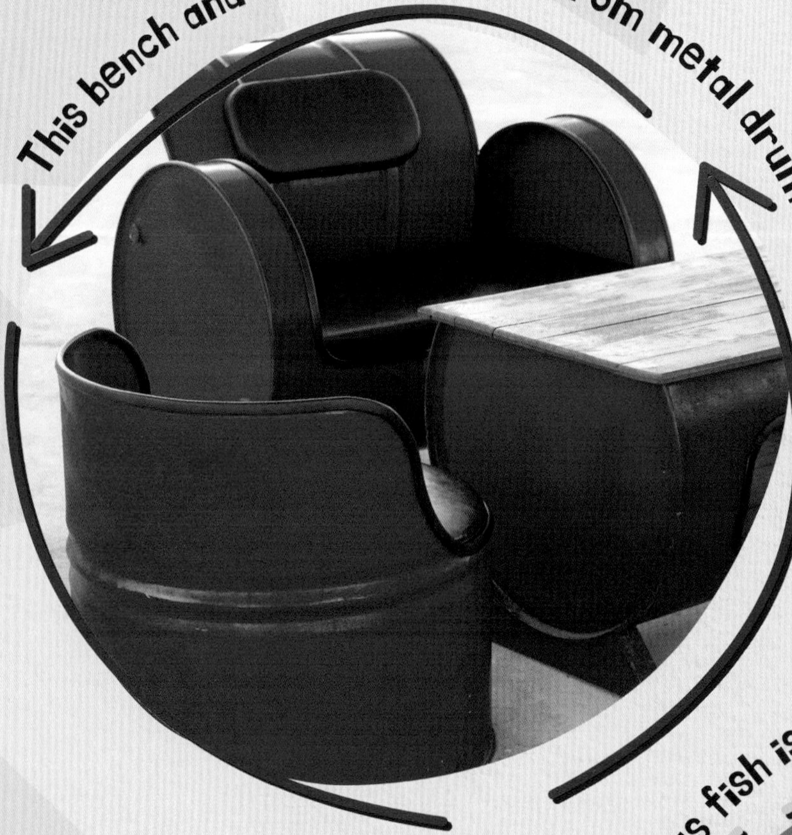

This bench and chair are made from metal drums!

This polar bear is made from old washing machines!

This fish is made from old car parts!

Make sure you get as much use out of your metal things as you can before recycling them.

TERRIFIC TINS

These lovely decorated cans can hold all sorts of useful things. Make them to match your room – or you could give them as a gift!

Even back in ancient times, people would recycle metal by melting it down to make new things.

You will need:

- Empty cans
- Glue
- Paint
- Paintbrushes
- String
- Ribbons and trims
- Decorations

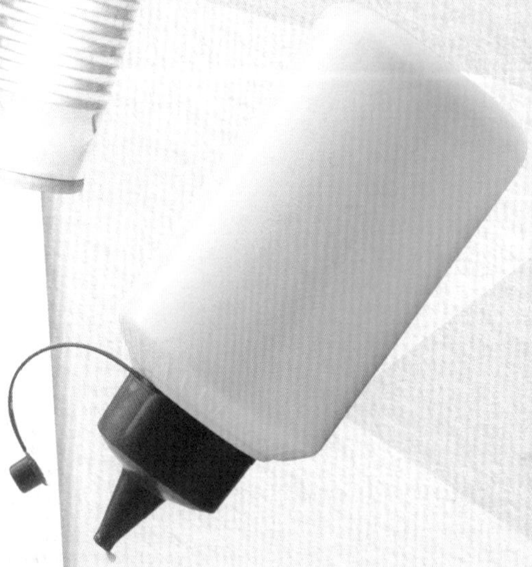

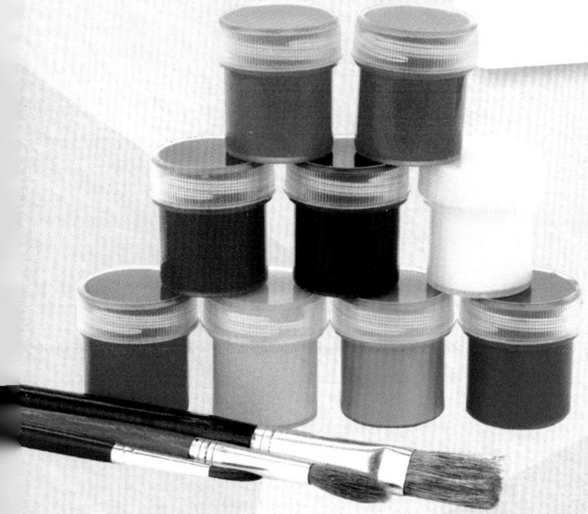

Safety First!

Remember to always make sure your cans are clean and dry. Make sure an adult has checked they are not sharp.

STEP 1. Paint all your cans white.

STEP 2. Leave your cans to dry.

STEP 3. Now it's time to get creative! Paint, glue, stick, tie, twist... how will you decorate yours?

Beautiful buttons?

A paper puppy?

You could cover your can in glue and roll it in torn up tissue paper... or how about wooden sticks and natural materials?

The natural look?

Perfect pipe cleaners?

If you don't need them anymore, remember to separate everything and recycle what you can!

PLANT IN A CAN

Tin cans make lovely plant pots and vases.

You will need:

- Empty cans
- Paint
- Decorations
- Paintbrushes
- Glue

Safety First!

Tin cans are sharp. Ask a grown-up to help you make sure it is safe to use.

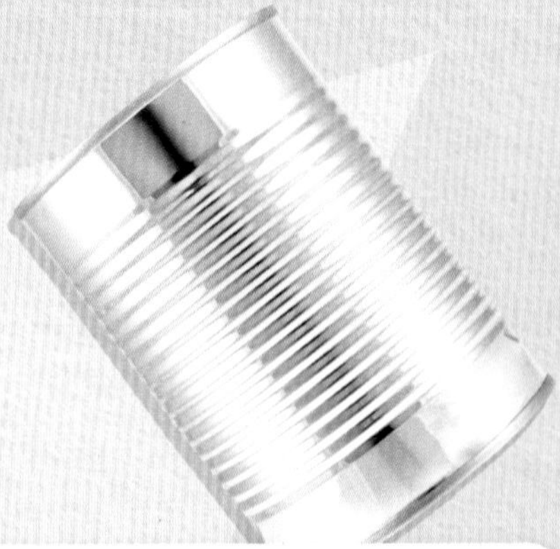

STEP 1. Find an old tin can and make sure it's clean.

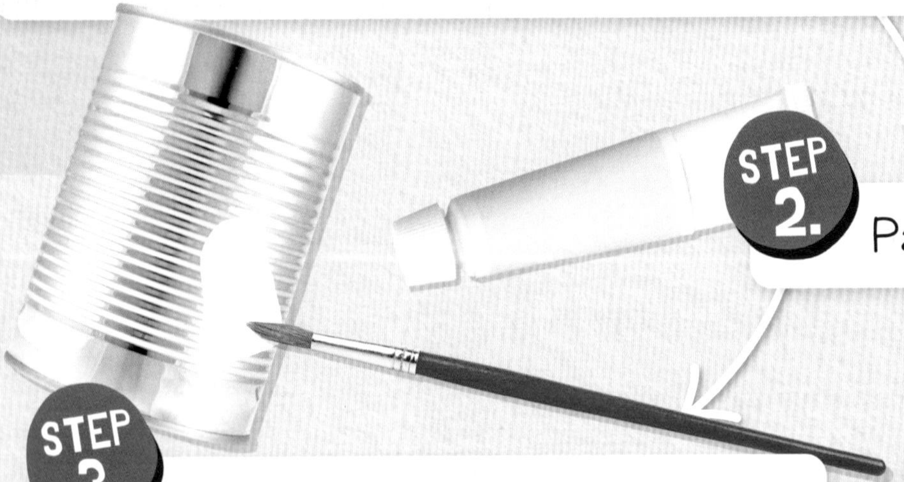

STEP 2. Paint the outside of your can.

STEP 3. When the paint is dry, decorate it with paper, material, string, ribbon or even pebbles!

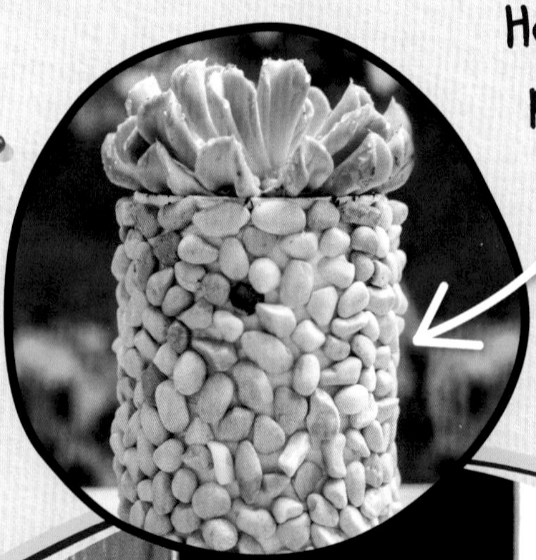
How about pebbles?

Simple and dotty?

STEP 4. Fill your can with soil or water, and put your plant or flowers in.